Benjamin Franklin
A Guide to the Exhibition

Exhibition Project Team

Page Talbott
CHIEF CURATOR

Melissa Clemmer
ASSISTANT CURATOR

CONTRIBUTORS
Barbara Fahs Charles
Dana Devon
David Gelles
Constance V. Hershey
Brent Kissel
Geoff Manaugh
Allison McBride
Rosalind Remer
Nicola Twilley

Staples & Charles, Ltd.
EXHIBITION DESIGNER

A More Perfect Union, LLC
MULTIMEDIA PRODUCER

Proto Productions, Inc.
EXHIBITION FABRICATOR

December 2005–March 2008

National Constitution Center, Philadelphia
Missouri Historical Society, St. Louis
Houston Museum of Natural Science
Denver Museum of Nature & Science
Atlanta History Center
Musée des Arts et Métiers and Musée Carnavalet, Paris

DESIGN: ALAIN SAINSON FRANK
PRODUCTION COORDINATOR: ANGELA TSANG
PRODUCED FOR THE BENJAMIN FRANKLIN TERCENTENARY BY
THE PHILADELPHIA MUSEUM OF ART • WHOLESALE AND RETAIL OPERATIONS DEPARTMENT
P.O. BOX 7646, PHILADELPHIA PA, 19101
ISBN 0-87633-192-4
© 2005 BY THE BENJAMIN FRANKLIN TERCENTENARY, PHILADELPHIA, PENNSYLVANIA

Dost thou love Life?
then do not squander Time;
for that's the Stuff Life is made of.

—*Poor Richard's Almanack, 1746*

Benjamin Franklin:
In Search of a Better World

Scientist, inventor, diplomat, humorist, philanthropist, and entrepreneur: Benjamin Franklin is one of the most remarkable and influential Americans of any generation. In this exhibition, created in honor of Franklin's 300th birthday, we invite you to experience the adventures of an extraordinary man.

You will meet Franklin in Boston, as a rebellious, ambitious teenager, and then travel with him to Philadelphia, London, and Paris. As you recreate Franklin's scientific experiments and civic initiatives, you'll have the chance to see the world through his ever-curious eyes. Finally, face to face with original copies of five of America's founding documents—all of which Franklin signed—you can practice your own skills at negotiation and compromise. Surrounded by Franklin's own possessions—many of which have been handed down in his family and never before seen in public—you'll be immersed in his world. As you are introduced to many aspects of Franklin that you never knew, you will also discover his impact on your own world.

Robert Feke
Portrait of Benjamin Franklin, 1738–1746
Oil on canvas
Harvard University Portrait Collection,
bequest of Dr. John Collins Warren, 1856,
Cambridge, Mass.
Descended in the family of John Franklin

Widely accepted as the earliest known likeness of Benjamin Franklin, this portrait has occasionally been thought to have been of his brother John, as it descended in his family. Robert Feke—a painter who worked in Boston, Philadelphia, and cities in between—portrayed Benjamin Franklin as a well-to-do gentleman in a traditional pose. Franklin was probably approaching retirement from his printing business, by which time he had already acquired an ample fortune.

I voluntarily offer'd and gave all my Money for it.

From *The Whistle*, an animation produced by A More Perfect Union, LLC, for the exhibition, with detail from portrait of Francis Folger Franklin attributed to Samuel Johnson; Private Collection.

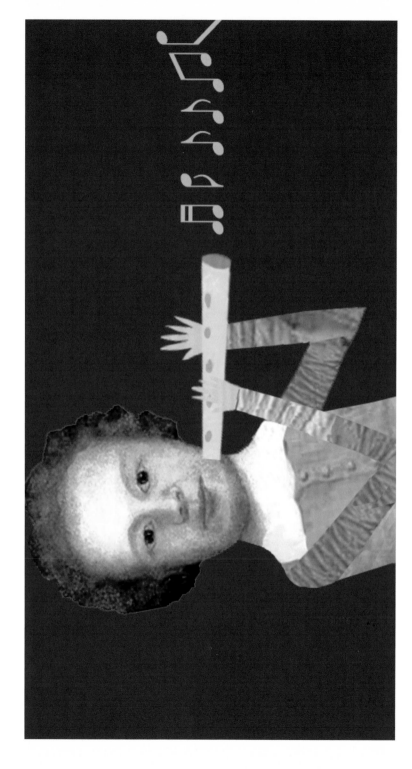

Franklin loved to tell stories, frequently using his youthful adventures to make a moral point. In *The Whistle*, young Benjamin's delight with his new toy turns to dismay once he learns that he paid too much for it. As he grew older, Franklin used this childhood lesson to question the inflated value people often place on status, wealth and possessions.

Being ignorant is not so much a Shame,
as being unwilling to learn.

—*Poor Richard's Almanack,* 1755

1706–1723
Character Matters

Born into a large family of Boston tradesmen, Benjamin Franklin learned early that hard work, thrift, integrity, and self-discipline were important personal virtues. Though Franklin attended school for only two years, he turned to books for reference, self-education, and delight. He was well-read in the religious and moral teachings of Boston's Puritan leadership, and he modeled his own writing on famous philosophers and essayists.

At 12, Benjamin was apprenticed to his older brother James, a printer. Franklin learned the trade easily and well, but ambition got the better of him. Brilliant and independent, he ran away from Boston when he was only 17. Franklin traveled first to New York but, finding no work, continued on to Philadelphia.

Curious and Ambitious

Franklin's mind was alight with energy, curiosity, and ambition, and all through his apprenticeship, he dreamed of running away, perhaps even going to sea. To cope with his frustration, Franklin charted out his days, hoping to use his time more efficiently and better his prospects. He ate healthfully; kept himself fit, particularly by swimming; taught himself to write by copying essays from newspapers; and soon produced his first published piece, the witty "Silence Dogood" letters.

Seeking Opportunity

In Franklin's time, apprenticeships were the common method by which a young man learned a trade. Fathers most often paid to have their sons apprenticed, and the more lucrative the trade, the higher the fee. Upon completion of this apprenticeship—which could take up to nine years—a worker was free to move to wherever there was business. Given the colonies' small population, markets for skilled labor were limited, and movement between cities was common.

Franklin's talent and ambition made his relationship with his brother James difficult, so rather than finish his printing apprenticeship, he ran away from Boston to look for a city in which his talent might flourish. On September 23, 1723, he sailed secretly for New York, looking for work with the nearest printer. Finding no position there, he traveled on to Philadelphia, where he arrived on October 6.

From *Seeking Opportunity*, a computer interactive produced by A More Perfect Union, LLC, for the exhibition.

With only your chandler apprenticeship freedom papers and a small amount of savings, you have decided to make your way to Philadelphia, one of the fastest-growing cities in the colonies. It's a long trip that could take many days.

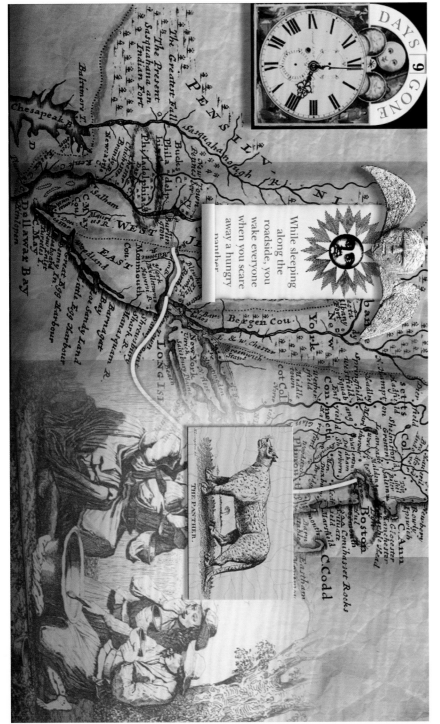

While sleeping along the roadside, you wake everyone when you scare away a hungry panther.

M. T. CICERO's

CATO MAJOR,

OR HIS

DISCOURSE

OF

OLD-AGE:

With Explanatory NOTES.

PHILADELPHIA:

Printed and Sold by B. FRANKLIN, MDCCXLIV.

He that hath a Trade,
hath an Estate.

—*Poor Richard's Almanack*, 1742

1723–1748
B. Franklin, Printer

Within just a few years of arriving in Philadelphia, Franklin established his own shop, printing jobs for many customers and publishing his newspaper, *The Pennsylvania Gazette*, and his *Poor Richard's Almanack*. In addition, Franklin and his wife Deborah sold stationery and dry goods from a store in front of the printing office. Franklin was honest and hard-working, and his growing reputation soon attracted customers away from rival printers.

To expand, Franklin set up several of his former apprentices with printing equipment and capital, enabling them to start their own businesses elsewhere in the colonies. He also maintained close ties with bookbinders, who helped to distribute his publications. Franklin even invested in several paper mills, and extended his reach into the German-speaking backcountry of Pennsylvania by financing a German-language printing office.

Cicero, translated by James Logan
M.T. Cicero's Cato Major
Philadelphia: Benjamin Franklin, 1744
Collection of Stuart E. Karu
Photo by Peter Harholdt

Franklin printed this book at his own expense to flatter James Logan, William Penn's secretary and one of Pennsylvania's most powerful and learned men. *Cato Major* is considered to be the finest example of Franklin's printing.

Compose your name.

1. Place your finger on a letter in the type case, and drag it to the composing stick. Repeat, until you have spelled your name.

YOUR NAME

From *Printer's Apprentice*, a computer interactive produced by A More Perfect Union, LLC, for the exhibition.

Apprentices in the printing trade needed to be hardworking, dexterous, and dedicated in order to complete their apprenticeship with skills necessary to begin their own careers. Setting type accurately and elegantly was the most complex part of their training.

This activity and others can be found at www.benfranklin300.org. Try practicing this type-setting exercise at home and print a copy to keep.

*In order to secure my Credit and Character as a Tradesmen,
I took care not only to be in Reality Industrious & frugal,
but to avoid all Appearances of the Contrary.*

—Benjamin Franklin, *Autobiography*

Job Printing

In 1730 Franklin opened a printing shop where he printed "jobs"—books and pamphlets published at the request and expense of others, usually organizations and individual authors. By 1748, when Franklin retired from business, he had printed numerous pamphlets and broadsides, and 432 books of which 241 were financed by others.

Although Franklin spent the second half of his life as a gentleman of leisure, he remained proud of his roots as a tradesman. Of course, for Franklin, "leisure" meant the freedom to pursue his many other interests, a freedom bought by years of devotion to the craft of printing. Perhaps this is why, of all his many accomplishments, he most wished to be remembered as "B. Franklin, Printer."

Ink balls (American), ca. 1740
Wood, wool, and sheepskin
The Frankliniana Collection,
The Franklin Institute, Inc., Philadelphia
Photo by Peter Harholdt
Owned by Benjamin Franklin;
descended in the Bache family

Using the ink balls, pieces of solid ink were mixed with a small amount of water on the surface of the ink stone, until the ink was of a uniform consistency. Then, with an ink ball in each hand, the pressman picked up the ink and applied it to the metal type with a dabbing, rolling, and beating motion before each pull of the press.

B. Franklin, Publisher

Franklin also achieved financial success as a publisher, and it is through his publishing activities that he gained early fame. He stole customers away from his rivals by spicing up the content of his newspapers and almanacs. He used his press to initiate debates that kept customers returning for more.

However, Franklin allowed no space for libel or personal abuse in his newspapers, avowing, "that having contracted with my Subscribers to furnish them with what might be either useful or entertaining, I could not fill their Papers with private Altercation . . . without doing them manifest Injustice."

Benjamin Franklin
Poor Richard, 1733
Philadelphia: Printed and sold by
B. Franklin, [1732]
Rosenbach Museum & Library, Philadelphia
Photo by Peter Harholdt

This is the only known copy of the first issue of *Poor Richard's Almanack*, an instant best-seller. Franklin, writing as the humble and henpecked Poor Richard, skillfully combined useful information—astronomical and meteorological predictions—with entertainment, in the form of proverbs, humor, and poetry.

The Pennsylvania Gazette,
no. 422, January 6–13, 1736/37
Philadelphia: Benjamin Franklin, 1736/37
Rare Book & Manuscript Library,
University of Pennsylvania, Philadelphia
Photo by Peter Harholdt

Owned, edited, and printed by Franklin from 1729 to 1748, the *Gazette* was known for its humor, originality, and strong influence on public opinion.

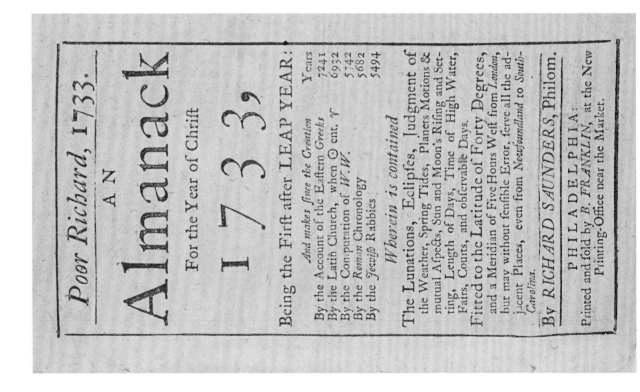

Nothing more like a Fool than a drunken Man.
Poor Richard.

'T IS an old Remark, that Vice always endeavours to assume the Appearance of Virtue: Thus Covetousness calls itself *Prudence*; *Prodigality* would be thought *Generosity*; and so of others. This perhaps arises hence, that Mankind naturally and universally approve Virtue in their Hearts, and detest Vice; and therefore, whenever thro' Temptation they fall into a Practice of the latter, they would if possible conceal it from themselves as well as others, under some other Name than that which properly belongs to it.

But DRUNKENNESS is a very unfortunate Vice in this respect. It bears no kind of Similitude with any sort of Virtue, from which it might possibly borrow a Name; and is therefore reduc'd to the wretched Necessity of being express'd by distant round-about Phrases, and of perpetually varying those Phrases, as often as they come to be well understood to signify plainly that A MAN IS DRUNK.

Tho' every one may possibly recollect a Dozen at least of the Expressions us'd on this Occasion, yet I think no one who has not much frequented Taverns would imagine the number of them so great as it really is. It may therefore surprize as well as divert the sober Reader, to have the Sight of a new Piece, lately communicated to me, entitled

The DRINKERS DICTIONARY.

A
He is Addled,
He's casting up his Accounts,
He's Affected,
He's in his Airs.

B
He's Biggy,
Bewitch'd,
Block and Block,
Boozy,
Bowz'd,
Been at Barbadoes,
Piss'd in the Brook,
Drunk as a Wheel-Barrow,
Burdock'd,
Buskey,
Buzzey,
Has Stole a Manchet out of the Brewer's Basket,
His Head is full of Bees,
Has been in the Bibbing Plot,
Has drank more than he has bled,
He's Bungey,
As Drunk as a Beggar,
He sees the Bears,
He's kiss'd black Betty,

C
He's Cat,
Cagrin'd,
Capable,
Cherubimical,
Cherry Merry,
Wamble Crop'd,
Crack'd,
Concern'd,
Half Way to Concord,
Has taken a Chirriping-Glass,
Got Corns in his Head,
A Cup to much,
Coguy,
Copey,
He's heat his Copper,
He's Crocus,
Catch'd,
He cuts his Capers,
He's been in the Cellar,
He's in his Cups,
Non Compos,
Cock'd,
Curv'd,
Cut,
Chipper,
Chickery,
Loaded his Cart,
He's been too free with the Creature,
Sir Richard has taken off his Confiding Cap,
He's Chap fallen,

D
He's Disguiz'd,
He's got a Dish,
Kill'd his Dog,
Took his Drops,
It is a Dark Day with him,
He's a Dead Man,
Has Dipp'd his Bill,
He's Dagg'd,
He's seen the Devil,

E
He's Prince Eugene,
Enter'd,
Wet both Eyes,
Cock Ey'd,
Got the Pole Evil,
Got a brass Eye,
Made an Example,

He's had a Thump over the Head with Sampson's Jawbone,
He's his Ear a Toad & half for Breakfast.

F
He's Fishey,
Fox'd,
Fuddled,
Sore Footed,
Frozen,
Well in for't,
Owes no Man a Farthing,
Fears no Man,
Crump Footed,
Been to France,
Flush'd,
Froze his Mouth,
Fetter'd,
Been to a Funeral,
His Flag is out,
Fuzl'd,
Spoke with his Friend,
Been at an Indian Feast.

G
He's Glad,
Groatable,
Gold-headed,
Glaiz'd,
Generous,
Booz'd the Gage,
As Dizzy as a Goose,
Been before George,
Got the Gout,
Had a Kick in the Guts,
Been with Sir John Goa,
Been at Geneva,
Globular,
Got the Glanders.

H
Half and Half,
Hardy,
Top Heavy,
Got by the Head,
Hiddey,
Got on his little Hat,
Hammerish,
Loose in the Hilts,
Knows not the way Home,
Got the Hornson,
Haunted with Evil Spirits,
Has Taken Hippocrates grand Elixir,

I
He's Intoxicated,
Jolly,
Jagg'd,
Jambled,

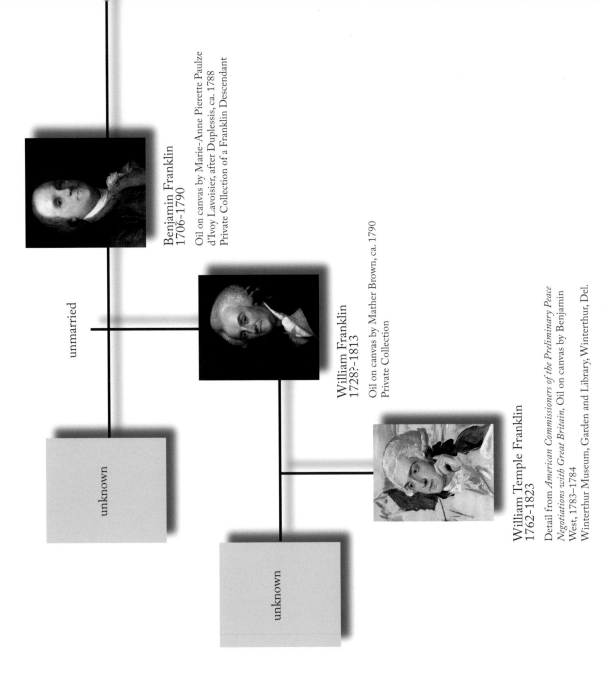

Benjamin Franklin
1706–1790

Oil on canvas by Marie-Anne Pierrette Paulze
d'Ivoy Lavoisier, after Duplessis, ca. 1788
Private Collection of a Franklin Descendant

unmarried

unknown

William Franklin
1728?–1813

Oil on canvas by Mather Brown, ca. 1790
Private Collection

unknown

William Temple Franklin
1762–1823

Detail from *American Commissioners of the Preliminary Peace
Negotiations with Great Britain*, Oil on canvas by Benjamin
West, 1783–1784
Winterthur Museum, Garden and Library, Winterthur, Del.

At Home with Benjamin Franklin

Franklin's relationship with his common-law wife, Deborah, was affectionate and loyal, if not particularly romantic. Deborah was involved in all aspects of the daily business, keeping the shop and its accounts. She raised William, Francis, and Sally in a crowded home typical of 18th-century artisans. Over the course of their marriage, Deborah and Benjamin Franklin shared their house with Deborah's mother, Sarah Read, their children, grandchildren, and an evolving mixture of relatives, houseguests, boarders, slaves and servants.

THE Pennsylvania GAZETTE.

Containing the freshest Advices Foreign and Domestick.

From January 6. to January 13. 1736,7.

Numb. 422.

Nothing more like a Fool than a drunken Man. Poor Richard.

IT IS an old Remark, that Vice always endeavours to assume the Appearance of Virtue: Thus Covetousness calls itself *Prudence*; *Prodigality* would be thought *Generosity*; and so of others. This perhaps arises hence, that Mankind naturally and universally approve Virtue in their Hearts, and detest Vice; and therefore, whenever thro' Temptation they fall into a Practice of the latter, they would if possible conceal it from themselves as well as others, under some other Name than that which properly belongs to it.

But DRUNKENNESS is a very unfortunate Vice in this respect. It bears no kind of Similitude with any sort of Virtue, from which it might possibly borrow a Name; and is therefore reduc'd to the wretched Necessity of being express'd by distant round-about Phrases, and of perpetually varying those Phrases, as often as they come to be well understood to signify plainly that A MAN IS DRUNK.

Tho' every one may possibly recollect a Dozen at least of the Expressions us'd on this Occasion, yet I think no one who has not much frequented Taverns would imagine the number of them so great as it really is. It may therefore surprize as well as divert the sober Reader, to have the Sight of a new Piece, lately communicated to me, entitled

The DRINKERS DICTIONARY.

A

He is Addled,
He's casting up his Accounts,
He's Afflicted,
He's in his Airs.

B

He's Biggy,
Bewitch'd,
Block and Block,
Boozy,
Bowz'd,
Been at Barbadoes,
Piss'd in the Brook,
He's Bungey,
As Drunk as a Beggar,
He sees the Bears,
He's kiss'd black Betty,
He's had a Thump over the Head with Sampson's Jaw-bone,
He's Bridgey,

C

He's Cat,
Cagrin'd,
Capable,
Cherubimical,
Cherry Merry,
Wamble Crop'd,
Crack'd,
Concern'd,
Half Way to Concord,
Has taken a Chirriping-Glass,
Got Corns in his Head,
A Cup to much,
Coguy,
Copey,
He's heat his Copper,
He's Crocus,
Catch'd,
He cuts his Capers,
He's been in the Cellar,
He's in his Cups,
Non Compos,
Cock'd,
Curv'd,
Cut,
Chipper,
Chickery,
Loaded his Cart,
He's been too free with the Creature,
Sir Richard has taken off his Considering Cap,
He's Chap fallen,

D

He's Disguiz'd,
He's got a Dish,
Kill'd his Dog,
Took his Drops,
It is a Dark Day with him,
He's a Dead Man,
Has Dipp'd his Bill,
He's Dagg'd,
He's seen the Devil,

E

He's Prince Eugene,
Enter'd,
Wet both Eyes,
Cock Ey'd,
Got the Pole Evil,
Got a brass Eye,
Made an Example,
He's Eat a Toad & half for Breakfast.
In his Element,

F

He's Fishey,
Fox'd,
Fuddled,
Sore Footed,
Frozen,
Well in for't,
Owes no Man a Farthing,
Fears no Man,
Crump Footed,
Been to France,
Flush'd,
Froze his Mouth,
Fetter'd,
Been to a Funeral,
His Flag is out,
Fuzl'd,
Spoke with his Friend,
Been at an Indian Feast.

G

He's Glad,
Groatable,
Gold-headed,
Glaiz'd,
Generous,
Booz'd the Gage,
As Dizzy as a Goose,
Been before George,
Got the Gout,
Had a Kick in the Guts,
Been with Sir John Goa,
Been at Geneva,
Globular,
Got the Glanders.

H

Half and Half,
Hardy,
Top Heavy,
Got by the Head,
Hiddey,
Got on his little Hat,
Hammerish,
Loose in the Hilts,
Knows not the way Home,
Got the Hornson,
Haunted with Evil Spirits,
Has Taken Hippocrates grand Elixir,

I

He's Intoxicated,
Jolly,
Jagg'd,
Jambled,

Going

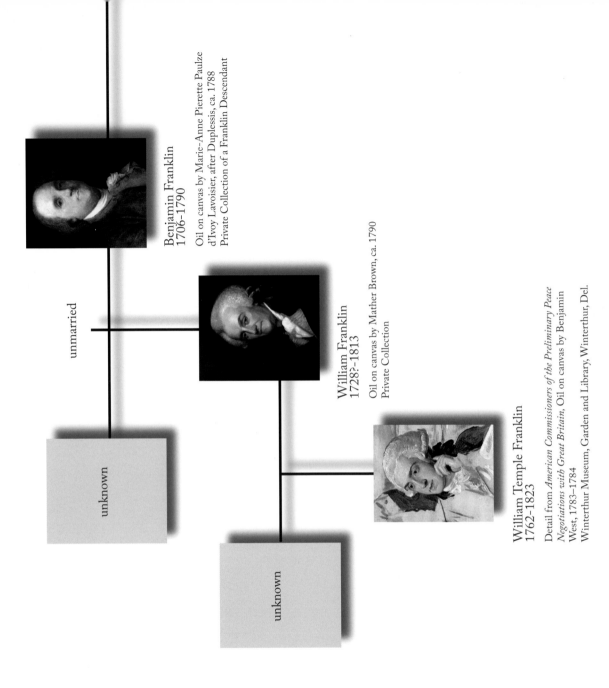

Benjamin Franklin
1706–1790

Oil on canvas by Marie-Anne Pierrette Paulze d'Ivry Lavoisier, after Duplessis, ca. 1788
Private Collection of a Franklin Descendant

unmarried

unknown

William Franklin
1728?–1813

Oil on canvas by Mather Brown, ca. 1790
Private Collection

unknown

William Temple Franklin
1762–1823

Detail from *American Commissioners of the Preliminary Peace Negotiations with Great Britain*, Oil on canvas by Benjamin West, 1783–1784
Winterthur Museum, Garden and Library, Winterthur, Del.

At Home with Benjamin Franklin

Franklin's relationship with his common-law wife, Deborah, was affectionate and loyal, if not particularly romantic. Deborah was involved in all aspects of the daily business, keeping the shop and its accounts. She raised William, Francis, and Sally in a crowded home typical of 18th-century artisans. Over the course of their marriage, Deborah and Benjamin Franklin shared their house with Deborah's mother, Sarah Read, their children, grandchildren, and an evolving mixture of relatives, houseguests, boarders, slaves and servants.

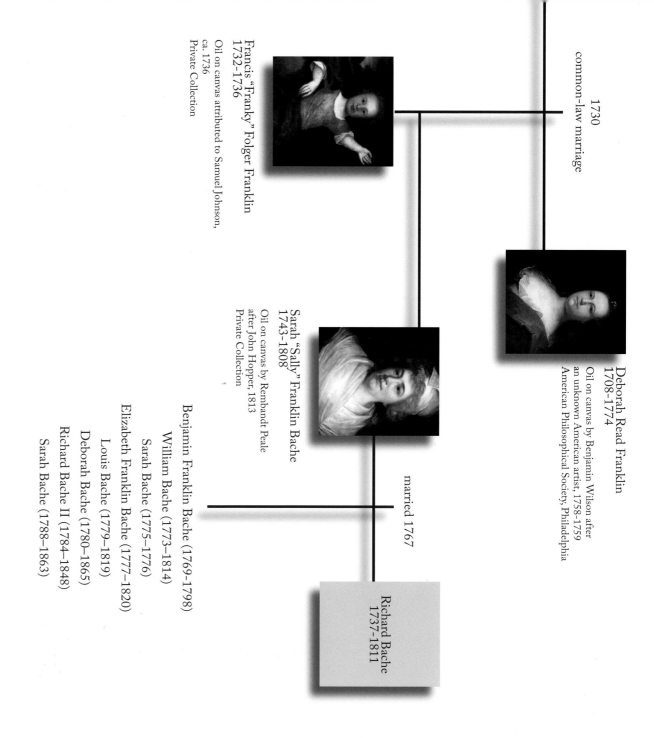

1730
common-law marriage

Deborah Read Franklin
1708-1774
Oil on canvas by Benjamin Wilson after
an unknown American artist, 1758-1759
American Philosophical Society, Philadelphia

Francis "Franky" Folger Franklin
1732-1736
Oil on canvas attributed to Samuel Johnson,
ca. 1736
Private Collection

Sarah "Sally" Franklin Bache
1743-1808
Oil on canvas by Rembandt Peale
after John Hopper, 1813
Private Collection

married 1767

Richard Bache
1737-1811

Benjamin Franklin Bache (1769-1798)
William Bache (1773-1814)
Sarah Bache (1775-1776)
Elizabeth Franklin Bache (1777-1820)
Louis Bache (1779-1819)
Deborah Bache (1780-1865)
Richard Bache II (1784-1848)
Sarah Bache (1788-1863)

Though William was Franklin's illegitimate son, Deborah brought him up as part of the family. Francis, their first child together, contracted smallpox as a toddler and died, which caused his parents deep and lasting grief. Their youngest child, Sally, was only 14 when Franklin was dispatched to London by the Pennsylvania Assembly, but she adored him and looked after him when he returned to Philadelphia as an old man. She would ultimately bear all but one of the Franklins' eight grandchildren.

Frugality is an enriching virtue,
a virtue I could never acquire in myself,
but I was lucky enough to find it in a wife,
who thereby became a fortune to me.

—Letter from Benjamin Franklin to Berthia Alexander, 1782

for which she had no other excuse or Apology to make, but that she thought her Husband deserv'd a Silver Spoon and China Bowl as well as any of his Neighbours.

From *A China Bowl with a Spoon of Silver*, an animation produced by A More Perfect Union, LLC, for the exhibition, with details from portraits of Benjamin and Deborah Franklin by Benjamin Wilson; Diplomatic Reception Rooms, U.S. Department of State, Washington, D.C., and American Philosophical Society, Philadelphia.

A China Bowl with a Spoon of Silver

Franklin and Deborah lived simply and frugally. Only after Franklin had established himself with a dependable income did they buy more extravagant possessions, often from Europe. Many of these objects are still owned by Franklin's descendants.

Later, in his autobiography, Franklin described one of the first of his fashionable household acquisitions—a china bowl and a spoon of silver. They are reunited in this exhibition for the first time in over 100 years.

Famille Rose bowl (Chinese), 1760–1770
Hard-paste porcelain
The Frankliniana Collection,
The Franklin Institute, Inc., Philadelphia
Photo by Peter Harholdt
Owned by Benjamin Franklin; descended
in the family of William Bache until the
early 19th century

Ebenezer Coker
Spoon (London), 1771–1772
Silver
Rare Book & Manuscript Library,
University of Pennsylvania, Philadelphia
Photo by Peter Harholdt
Owned by Benjamin Franklin; descended
in the family of Deborah Bache Duane

The Ingenious Dr. Franklin

When Franklin saw an unmet need, he often created or adapted a device to satisfy it. Visitors to Franklin's house recorded the useful "curiosities" they saw there, such as the chair/stepstool, table/firescreen, "long arm" pole (to reach books), and, as Franklin's friend Manassah Cutler observed, "his great armed chair, with rocker and a large fan placed over it, with which he fans himself . . . with only a small motion of his foot." Franklin is also credited with inventing bifocals, or "double spectacles," as he called them.

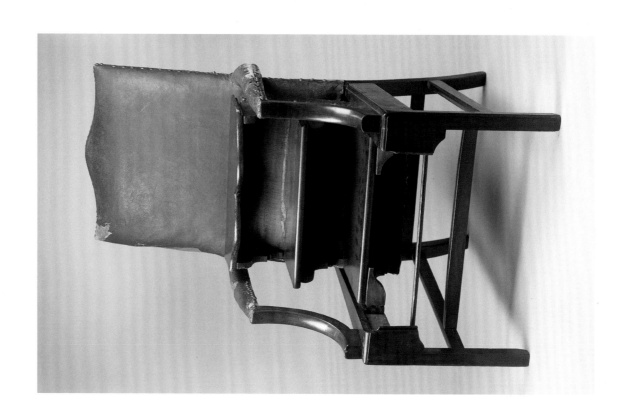

Possibly designed by Benjamin Franklin
Library chair with folding steps
(London or Philadelphia), 1760–1780
Mahogany, leather, and steel
American Philosophical Society, Philadelphia
Photo by Peter Harholdt

Owned by Benjamin Franklin; given to the
American Philosophical Society by Franklin's
son-in-law Richard Bache in 1792

Benjamin Franklin and Slavery

Benjamin Franklin was a slaveholder for most of his life. The enslaved Africans who are mentioned in Franklin's correspondence include Peter, Jemima, Othello (who died young), King, and George. While he wrote in his 1757 will "that my Negro Man Peter, and his Wife Jenima, be free after my Decease," they died before Franklin, who did not own any slaves at the end of his life. In his later years Franklin became an ardent abolitionist, and in his final will Franklin stipulated that his son-in-law, Richard Bache, should not receive his inheritance unless he freed his slave, Bob.

—Letter from Benjamin Franklin to Josiah Wedgwood, 1787

I received the Letter . . . with your valuable Present of Cameo's, which I am distributing among my Friends, in whose Countenances I have seen such Marks of being affected by contemplating the Figure of the Suppliant, (which is admirably executed) that I am persuaded it may have an Effect equal to that of the best written Pamphlet, in procuring Favour to those oppressed People.

Designed by William Hackwood, made by the Wedgwood Factory
Am I Not a Man and a Brother?, ca. 1790
Stoneware, unglazed, white with black clay
American Philosophical Society, Philadelphia

Wedgwood produced these medallions to raise money for the abolitionists' cause. In 1788 some of the medallions were sent to Franklin in Philadelphia. This image became so popular that it was replicated in many formats, including buttons, sashes, and decorations on cups and pitchers.

Of this cameo medallion, Wedgwood wrote to Franklin: "It gives me great pleasure to be embarked on this occasion in the same great and good cause with you, and I ardently hope for the final completion of our wishes."

1 The Draw Bridge
2 Buds Building
3 Edw Shipen^s
4 Ant. Morris Brew Hou
5 Capt. Vineing^s
6 Ionathan Dickinson
7 John Witpe
8 Capt Antho
9 George Pai
10 Ios. Shipe
11 Wm Fisbourn
12 The Scal

Peter Cooper
The South East Prospect of the City of Philadelphia,
ca. 1718
Oil on canvas
Library Company of Philadelphia

This is the oldest surviving painting of a North American urban center. While it distorts a few of the buildings, the scene represents what Franklin may have seen when he first arrived in Philadelphia.

The Good particular Men may do separately…is small, compared with what they may do collectively.

—"Appeal for the Hospital," *The Pennsylvania Gazette*, 1751

1731–1751
Civic Visions

*The noblest question in the world is
What Good may I do in it?*

—*Poor Richard's Almanack, 1737*

Even as a young tradesman, Franklin sought to better himself and his community. He organized the Junto—a small group of fellow tradesmen and artisans committed to mutual improvement. At their weekly meetings they asked how they "may be serviceable to mankind? to their country, to their friends, or to themselves?" The Junto's actions formed their answer. Franklin and his colleagues helped establish a lending library, firefighting brigade, university, learned society, militia, hospital, and insurance company.

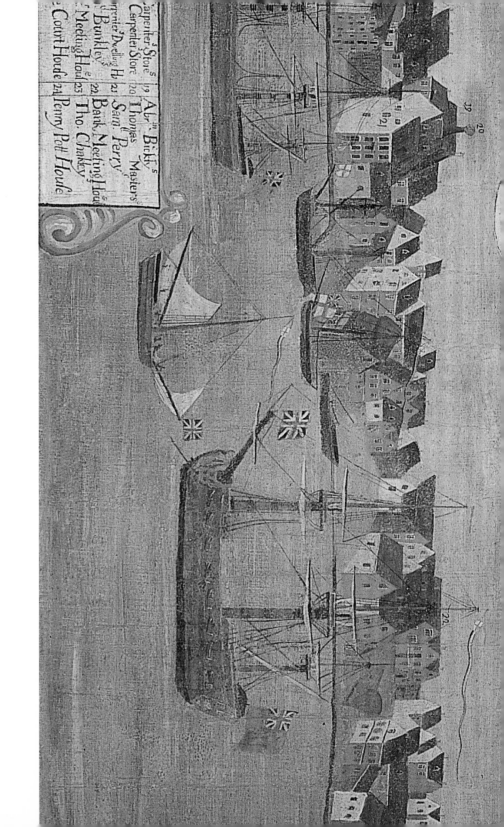

Carpenter's Store 19 Abr.^m Bickly^s
Carpenter's Store 20 Thomas Master's
Carpenter's Dwelling H.21 Saml Perry's
U. Brinkley 22 Bank Meeting Hou
Meeting Hou 23 Tho. Chalkey
CourtHouse 24 Perry Pott House

Franklin's lifelong efforts to improve himself and the world around him stemmed from the same ambition and intellectual energy he demonstrated as a printer and young boy. His commitment to public service also built on his sociable nature: Franklin was a true philanthropist. He believed that society's many challenges required mutual action, collaboration, and generosity. This, for Franklin, defined citizenship, in the colonies and in the young republic.

Improving the Self

Franklin placed great value on self-improvement. He believed that integrity and moral responsibility were the backbone of a successful life and a strong community. He examined his own behavior frequently and, at one point, outlined 12 virtues that needed his attention: temperance, silence, order, resolution, frugality, industry, sincerity, justice, moderation, cleanliness, tranquility, and chastity. A Quaker friend suggested a 13th—humility—but Franklin admitted: "I cannot boast of much Success in acquiring the *Reality* of this Virtue; but I had a good deal with regard to the *Appearance* of it." Franklin struggled throughout his life to live up to these ideals.

"Lion's Mouth" box, ca. 1750
Painted tin
Library Company of Philadelphia

The breadth of the collection of books at the Library Company was unique compared to the existing college libraries, which focused on theology. Books were selected by the readers themselves, reflecting their own interests and aspirations. The "Lion's Mouth" was their suggestion box.

As a lifelong learner, Franklin taught himself to read French, German, Italian, and Spanish, on top of the Latin he learned as a child. To help others educate themselves, he and his fellow Junto members founded the Library Company of Philadelphia, America's first subscription library, and the University of Pennsylvania, America's first nonsectarian college. Franklin believed that, above all, education should be useful, with an emphasis on character, hard work, and bodily and spiritual health.

The Philadelphia Academy

Franklin's self-education and religious tolerance made him challenge the dominant classical and theological approach to learning. Soon after his retirement, he helped found the Philadelphia Academy, which later became the University of Pennsylvania, America's first university. Unlike Harvard and Yale, the school was not created to train new ministers. Rather, with a progressive curriculum based solidly in the liberal arts, the University of Pennsylvania sought to develop a vigorous, public-spirited curiosity in each of its students.

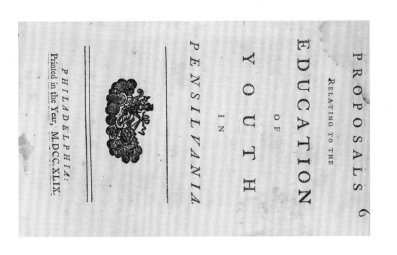

PROPOSALS 6

RELATING TO THE

EDUCATION

OF

YOUTH

IN

PENSILVANIA.

PHILADELPHIA:
Printed in the Year, M,DCC,XLIX.

Benjamin Franklin
Proposals Relating to the Education of Youth in Pensilvania
Philadelphia: Benjamin Franklin, 1749
Library Company of Philadelphia
Photo by Peter Harholdt

Franklin wrote this pamphlet in support of establishing Philadelphia's first institution of higher learning, wherein he declared that "the great Aim and End of all learning" is "to serve Mankind, one's Country, Friends and Family." He specified who should attend and what should be taught, supported with lengthy quotations from Locke, Milton and other philosophers. Additionally, Franklin set forth his recommendations on diet, exercise, and the benefits of swimming.

Protecting the Citizens

Franklin's drive to improve himself naturally spilled over into a desire to further the common good. His public spirit mixed with practical organizational skills to produce a variety of civic improvement schemes. Because Franklin's first priority was to see his ideas realized, he was always willing to cede credit to and collaborate with others.

Within just a few years, Franklin, with a group of like-minded citizens, helped found the Pennsylvania Hospital, America's first public hospital; the Union Fire Company, Philadelphia's first volunteer fire brigade; and the Philadelphia Contributionship, America's first property insurance company. No useful project was too small for his attention, from inventing a new street lamp that was easier to repair and clean, to designing his Pennsylvanian fire-place meant to conserve fuel and prevent tragic house fires.

Franklin's enduring concern for the general welfare of his fellow citizens was reflected in such diverse activities as his campaign to improve urban sanitation, as well as the formation of an all-volunteer militia to defend against the threat of war with France and its Native American allies.

John Stow
Philadelphia Contributionship fire mark,
1752–1753
Wood and lead
Smithsonian Institution, National
Museum of American History, Behring
Center, Washington, D.C.

At the first meeting of the Contributionship's Board of Directors in 1752, the silversmith Philip Syng, Jr., was asked to devise a seal for the company, "being four Hands united." This is the earliest issued fire mark to be affxed to houses to show that they were insured.

Whenever a FIRE breaks out in any Part of the City, though none of our Houses, Goods, or Effects may be in apparent Danger, we will nevertheless, repair thither with our Buckets and Bags . . . and give our utmost Assistance to such of our Fellow-Citizens as may stand in Need of it, in the same Manner as if they belonged to this Company.

—"Articles of the Union Fire-Company, of Philadelphia," 1794

the Place is crowded by active Men of different Ages, Professions and Titles; who, as of one Mind and Rank,

From *Brave Men at Fires*, an animation produced by A More Perfect Union, LLC, for the exhibition, with detail from *Certificate of the Hand-in-Hand Fire Company*, New York, possibly by Henry Dawkins; The New York Public Library.

Institutions and businesses kept buckets in good repair so staff could quickly respond to the outbreak of a fire. Members of each fire company were required to own several buckets; by 1767 the number of required buckets had risen to eight.

Fire bucket (American), late 18th–early 19th century, inscribed "Library Company of Philadelphia" Leather Library Company of Philadelphia Photo by Peter Harholdt

23

*What signifies knowing the Names,
if you know not the Natures of Things.*

—*Poor Richard's Almanack, 1750*

1747–1785
Useful Knowledge

Throughout his life, Franklin's curiosity and hands-on approach to his surroundings attracted him to science or "natural philosophy," as it was then called. A true man of the Enlightenment, Franklin's reasoning was practical and observation-based, and he shared his theories in letters to international contemporaries and colleagues. Franklin firmly believed that scientific knowledge should directly benefit society, so he never patented his inventions and always sought useful applications for the theories he developed.

Franklin's studies of electricity, including the legendary kite and key experiment, remain his most important and best known scientific achievements. Although he personally placed a higher value on public service than science, it was his scientific status that gave him the connections he needed to succeed in politics and diplomacy.

Designed by Benjamin Franklin
Top portion of a lightning rod, ca. 1756
Iron
The Frankliniana Collection,
The Franklin Institute, Inc., Philadelphia
Photo by Peter Harholdt

This rod, from the Wister house on High Street (now Market Street), Philadelphia, is believed to be one of the earliest lightning rods erected by Franklin. John Wister was an early convert to the value of lightning rods. The tip of his device was probably melted by a lightning strike and, weakened, it was subsequently bent by wind.

A Society of "Ingenious Men"

In an era before widespread public education, private discussion groups and learned societies were vital to a nation's cultural and intellectual growth. Franklin's Junto had already demonstrated how much friends committed to one another's mutual improvement could accomplish. In 1743 Franklin drew up a proposal to create an intercolonial Junto of sorts: a network of scientists and philosophers who would share news of their discoveries by post.

This idea became the American Philosophical Society, the oldest learned society in America. It was modeled after London's Royal Society and Dublin's Philosophical Society, and its six founding members included botanist John Bartram and lawyer-scientist Thomas Hopkinson. Fifty years later the Society included a host of prominent Philadelphia intellectuals, founding fathers George Washington, Thomas Jefferson, and John Adams, and such international figures as the Marquis de Lafayette. The Society provided a forum for exchanging ideas and pooling skills and knowledge, and its members particularly strove to promote American science and invention. Today the Society still plays an active role in America's intellectual life.

William Bartram
Illustration of the Franklinia alatamaha, 1788
Engraving
American Philosophical Society, Philadelphia

Named after Franklin, this flowering tree was discovered along the Altamaha River in Georgia in 1765 and saved from extinction. As one of John and William Bartram's most famous botanical discoveries, an image of the plant was subsequently published in William Bartram's *Travels through North & South Carolina, Georgia, East & West Florida* (Philadephia: Printed by James & Johnson, 1791).

FRANKLINIA *alatamaha Bart. Zearn.*

It is . . . proposed . . . That One Society be formed of Virtuosi or ingenious Men residing in the several Colonies, to be called The American Philosophical Society; who are to maintain a constant Correspondence.

—Benjamin Franklin, *A Proposal for Promoting Useful Knowledge*, 1743

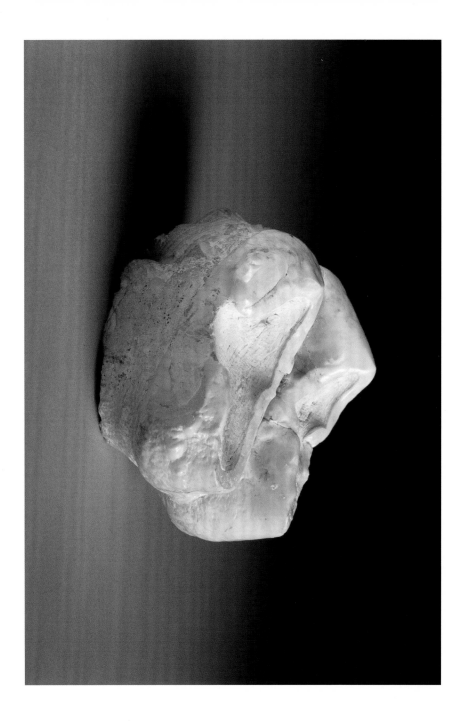

I should also be glad of the Piece of Elephant's Tooth. It is old Ivory, perhaps of the Time before the Flood, & would be a Rarity to some Friends here.

—Letter from Benjamin Franklin to Margaret Stevenson, 1779

Mastodon tooth fossil
Fossilized stone
Independence National Historical Park, Philadelphia
Photo by Peter Harholdt

Found near the underground ruins of Franklin's home on Market Street, this tooth matches the description of a "large pronged" tooth sent to Franklin in London in 1767 by Indian agent and land speculator George Croghan. Thought to derive from ancient elephant-like creatures, the fossils were discovered near the Ohio River at a place called "The Great Licking Place," now known as Big Bone Lick, Kentucky.

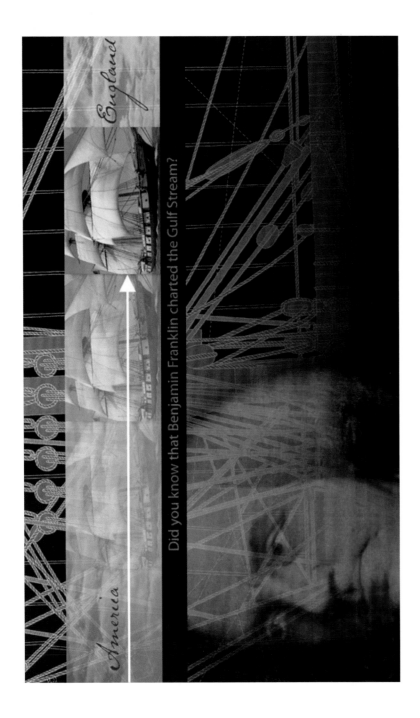

America

England

Did you know that Benjamin Franklin charted the Gulf Stream?

From *Charting the Gulf Stream*, a computer interactive produced by A More Perfect Union, LLC, for the exhibition, with detail from portrait of Benjamin Franklin by Mason Chamberlin; Philadelphia Museum of Art.

Shipboard Amusements

Never one to waste an opportunity or to pass the time unoccupied, Franklin used his multiple transatlantic journeys—which lasted weeks in each direction—to observe and study the natural phenomena around him. Franklin carefully recorded his observations, keeping journals filled with details documenting the origins of storms, the formation of lightning, and the effects of oil on water. His fascination with maritime weather led him to include meteorological information in his *Poor Richard's Almanack*, helping both travelers and colonial farmers prepare for shifting weather patterns.

Franklin also studied the transatlantic path of the Gulf Stream, charting its route with his cousin Timothy Folger, a Nantucket whaling captain. Their surprisingly accurate map has been widely used by seamen of many nations, reducing the lengthy ocean crossing and spurring interest in the mysteries of the Atlantic.

Having since crossed this stream several times in passing between America and Europe, I . . . know when one is in it; and besides the gulph weed with which it is interspersed, I find that it is always warmer than the sea on each side of it, and that it does not sparkle in the night.

—Benjamin Franklin, "Maritime Observations,"
Transactions of the American Philosophical Society, 1786

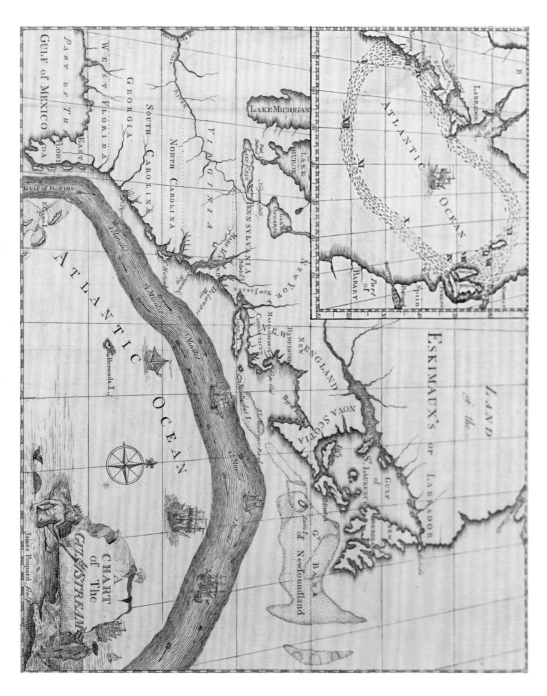

Chart of the Gulf Stream, from Benjamin Franklin, "Maritime Observations," in *Transactions of the American Philosophical Society,* 1786
American Philosophical Society, Philadelphia

Electrical Fire

The study of electricity was the most spectacular and fashionable branch of Enlightenment natural philosophy. Franklin was immediately hooked when the Library Company's British agent, Peter Collinson, sent him a glass tube used to generate static electricity. Franklin taught himself to perform basic electrical "tricks" with it and was soon immersed in trying to understand how this surprising phenomenon worked.

Through his electrical investigations, Franklin developed important new theories, complete with new terms and instruments to describe and demonstrate them. As usual, his concern centered on developing useful applications for his discoveries: the result was a lightning protection system that is still in use today, notably on St. Paul's Cathedral in London.

Franklin's experiments were known all over Europe, initially through his personal correspondence and then through publications initiated by colleagues abroad. Later, Franklin's international fame as a scientist would give him the status and political access to succeed as America's premier diplomat.

Broadside advertising Ebenezer Kinnersley's lectures on "Electrical Fire"
Newport: James Franklin, 1752
Rosenbach Museum & Library, Philadelphia
Photo by Peter Harholdt

Newport, March 16, 1752.

Notice is hereby given to the Curious,

That at the COURT-HOUSE, in the Council-Chamber, is now to be exhibited, and continued from Day to Day, for a Week or two;

A COURSE of EXPERIMENTS, on the newly-discovered

Electrical FIRE:

Containing, not only the most curious of those that have been made and published in *Europe*, but a considerable Number of new Ones lately made in *Philadelphia*; to be accompanied with methodical LECTURES on the Nature and Properties of that wonderful Element.

By *Ebenezer Kinnersley*.

LECTURE I.

I. OF Electricity in General, giving some Account of the Discovery of it.
II. That the Electric Fire is a real Element, and different from those heretofore known and named, and added out of other Matter (not created) by the Friction of Glass, &c.
IV. That it is doth not take up any perceptible Time in passing thro' large Portions of Space.
V. That it is intimately mixed with the Substance of all the other Fluids and Solids of our Globe.
VI. That our Bodies at all Times contain enough of it to set a House on Fire.
VIII. That it differs from common Matter, in this; that tho' it will fire inflammable Matters, itself has no sensible Heat.
IX. That is from common Matter, in this; its Parts do not mutually attract, but mutually repel each other.
IX. That it is strongly attracted by all other Matter.
X. An artificial Spider, animated by the Electric Fire, so as to act like a live One.
XI. A Shower of Sand, which rises again as fast as it falls.
XII. That common Matter in the Form of Points attracts this Fire more strongly than in any other Form.
XIII. A Leaf of the most weighty of Metals suspended in the Air, as is said of *Mahomet's* Tomb.
XIV. An Appearance like Fishes swimming in the Air.
XV. That this Fire will live in Water, a River not being sufficient to quench the smallest Spark of it.
XVI. A Representation of the Sensitive Plant.
XVII. A Representation of the seven Planets, shewing a probable Cause of their keeping their due Distances from each other, and from the Sun in the Center.
XVIII. The Salute replied by the Ladies Fire; or Fire darting from a Ladies Lips, so that she may defy any Person to salute her.
XIX. Eight musical Bells rung by an electrified Phial of Water.
XX. A Battery of eleven Guns discharged by Fire issuing out of a Person's Finger.

LECTURE II.

I. A Description and Explanation of Mr. *Musschenbroek's* wonderful Bottle.
II. The amazing Force of the Electric Fire in passing thro' a Number of Bodies at the same Instant.
III. An Electric Mine sprung.
IV. Electrified Money, which (scarce any Body will take when offer'd) to them.
V. A Piece of Money drawn out of a Person's Mouth in spite of his Teeth; yet without touching it, or offering him the least Violence.
VI. Spirits kindled by Fire darting from a Lady's Eyes (without a Metaphor).
VII. Various Representations of Lightning, the Cause and Effect of which will be explained by a more probable Hypothesis than has hitherto appeared, and some useful Instructions given, how to avoid the Danger of it: How to secure Houses, Ships, &c. from being hurt by its destructive Violence.
VIII. The Force of the Electric Spark, making a fair Hole thro' a Quire of Paper.
IX. Metal melted by it (tho' without any Heat) in less than a thousandth Part of a Minute.
X. Animals killed by it instantaneously.
XI. Air issuing out of a Bladder set on Fire by a Spark from a Person's Finger, and burning like a Volcano.
XII. A few Drops of electrified cold Water let fall on a Person's Hand, supplying him with Fire sufficient to kindle a burning Flame with one of the Fingers of his other Hand.
XIII. A Sulphureous Vapour kindled into Flame by Fire issuing out of a cold Apple.
XIV. A curious Machine acting by means of the Electric Fire, and playing Variety of Tunes on eight musical Bells.
XV. A Battery of eleven Guns discharged by a Spark, after it has passed through ten Foot of Water.

And, for the more effectually enlarging the human Mind, and giving it more noble and exalted Ideas of the Author of Nature, and fresh proofs of his Providence, assisting of Reason & Encouragement.

Lectures may to be had at the Houses of Mr. Allen, in Thames-Street, next Door to Mr. John Tweedy's, in T————s——. The Lectures to begin each Day precisely at Three o'Clock in the Afternoon. Price Thirty Shillings each Lecture.

Your kind present of an electric tube, with directions for using it, has put several of us on making electrical experiments, in which we have observed some particular phenomena that we look upon to be new. I was never before engaged in any study that so totally engrossed my attention and time.

—Letter from Benjamin Franklin to Peter Collinson, 1747

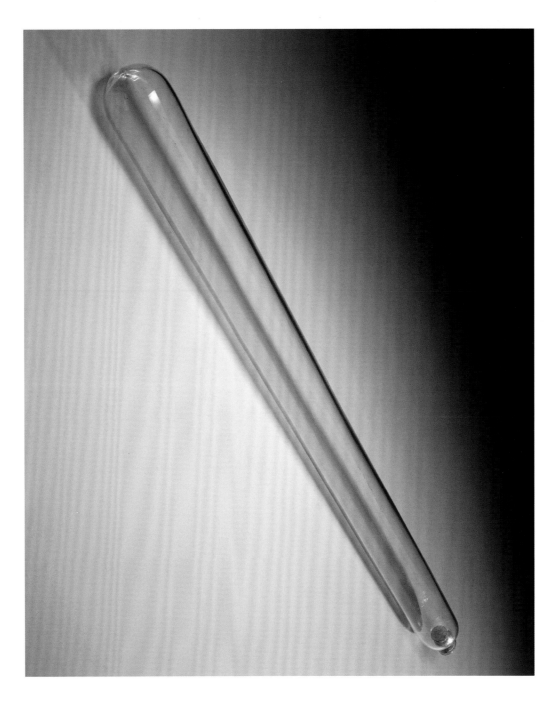

Static electricity tube, ca. 1747
Glass
The Frankliniana Collection,
The Franklin Institute, Inc., Philadelphia
Photo by Peter Harholdt
Owned by Benjamin Franklin; given to him by his friend
Peter Collinson

Ever the entrepreneur, Franklin encouraged his unemployed neighbor Kinnersley to become a traveling lecturer on electricity. His lectures, said to have been "pleasing to all sorts of people" and "very curious," constituted the first public announcement that grounded rods could protect structures from lightning. This broadside advertisement was printed by Franklin's nephew.

A Gentleman's Laboratory

In an era when scientists were almost always wealthy male amateurs, scientific breakthroughs occurred—frequently by chance—in home laboratories. Enthusiastic natural philosophers, including Franklin, would often demonstrate electrical experiments on their newly-purchased equipment as an entertaining party trick.

The laboratory equipment itself varied widely. Glass tubes, for instance, were rubbed with wool or fur to produce an electrical charge. The lightning bells, Franklin's own invention, were connected to an insulated rod atop a building; they would ring whenever an electrified cloud or lightning was nearby. The Leyden jar was the world's first capacitor. With metallic conductors mounted inside and outside a glass jar (the insulator), a Leyden jar could store and transport the electric charge that was produced by rubbing a glass tube, described above. Laboratories might also contain thermometers, pneumatic air pumps, magnets, and experimental clocks, all depending on the interests and resources of the natural philosopher who owned the lab.

"Electrical battery" of Leyden jars, 1760–1769
Glass, metal, and wood
American Philosophical Society, Philadelphia
Photo by Peter Harholdt
Owned by Benjamin Franklin

This set of Leyden jars descended in the family of Francis Hopkinson, Franklin's "ingenious friend," to whom he bequeathed the "philosophical instruments I have in Philadelphia." Hopkinson was also an executor of Franklin's will.

Mason Chamberlin, engraved by Edward Fisher
Benjamin Franklin of Philadelphia, L.L.D., F.R.S.,
1763
Mezzotint
Collection of Stuart E. Karu
Photo by Peter Harholdt

In one of his favorite likenesses, which he distributed to friends and relatives, Franklin is shown next
to the bells that he used to study thunderstorm
electricity. A grounded rod of his improved design
is shown in the background on the right.

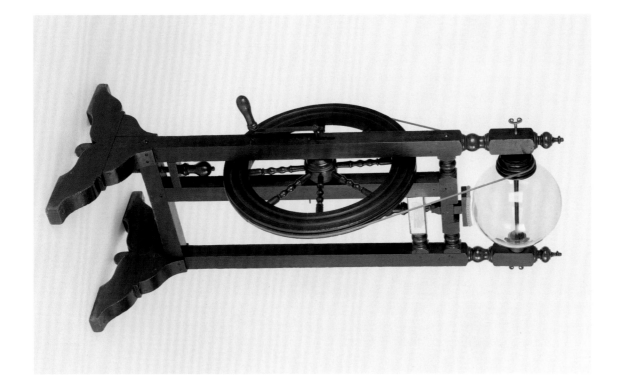

Designed by Benjamin Franklin,
made by Philadelphia-area craftsmen,
including Wistarburgh Glassworks, N.J.
Electrical Apparatus, 1742–1747
Walnut and iron
Library Company of Philadelphia
Owned by Benjamin Franklin; presented to the Library
Company by Benjamin Franklin Bache in 1792

Designed by Benjamin Franklin
"Join, or Die" from *The Pennsylvania Gazette*, May 9, 1754
Philadelphia: Benjamin Franklin, 1754
Library Company of Philadelphia

In May 1754, just before the Albany Conference, Franklin published this cut rattlesnake cartoon. It illustrated an editorial urging the colonies to join together against the French. This motif remained popular, reappearing in the period leading up to the Revolutionary War as a symbol of the strength of colonial unity against Great Britain.

Would you persuade,
speak of Interest, not of Reason.

—*Poor Richard's Almanack, 1734*

1744–1787
World Stage

Franklin was a master diplomat and negotiator, exercising restraint, flexibility, and compromise to bring opposing visions into accord. Whether negotiating with Native Americans in western Pennsylvania or with the great powers of England and France, Franklin drew on strategies of collaboration and mutual self-interest to forge alliances that shaped the future of America.

Franklin became a powerful force in the fight for independence, traveling to France to seek aid for America's struggle against Britain. In Paris, Franklin capitalized on his brilliant reputation and charm; his humble demeanor and natural wit served the American cause well, and he forged strong transatlantic ties. In the end, this international alliance resulted in victory after a long Revolutionary War.

Once back on American soil, Franklin brought a spirit of compromise and unity to the Constitutional Convention.

Forging Unification

The threat of war with French imperial forces and their Native American allies made it clear that military strength should best be sought through British colonial unity. Where others saw division, competition, and even chaos, Franklin saw an opportunity for the pursuit of common goals.

Franklin proposed the Albany Plan of Union in June 1754, when delegates from seven of the colonies met to secure the alliance of the Iroquois and plan for their mutual defense. Although his Plan was not adopted, Franklin's inclination to forge partnerships and his aversion to conflict remained characteristic of his approach to civic life, science, and diplomacy. His negotiating skills were further called into service in 1757, when Franklin was selected to represent colonial interests in England.

Franklin would spend much of the next 30 years of his life living abroad—first in London seeking to maintain unity with England, and then in Paris building an alliance to secure American independence.

ALBANY PLAN OF UNION, 1754

In 1754, as Britain and France struggled for control over North America, Benjamin Franklin proposed the Albany Plan of Union to unite the British North American colonies. His Plan called for the creation of a legislative body that would have the power to control commerce and organize defense in the face of attacks by the French or their Native American allies.

The Albany Plan was rejected by both the colonists and the British Crown. The Crown worried that the Plan would create a powerful colonial bloc that might prove difficult to control, while the colonists themselves did not yet recognize the value of intercolonial unity.

And tho' we were at first only tied together by a Rope, yet lest this Rope should grow Rotten and break, we tied ourselves together by an iron Chain—lest time and accident might rust and destroy this Chain of iron, we afterwards made one of Silver; the strength and brightness of which would be subject to no decay.

—Sir William Johnson, British Superintendent of Indian Affairs, speaking to the Six Nations, 1755

Keep Bright the Chain

Franklin's friend and physician in London, Dr. John Fothergill, gave him this jug, perhaps in 1775, engraved "Keep bright the chain." This motto, adopted by Franklin from treaties with Indians, refers to the chain of friendship between allies. Here Fothergill refers to their mutual efforts to maintain diplomatic relations without the need for war.

Daniel Smith and Robert Sharp
Milk jug, 1765
Silver
Sterling and Francine Clark Art Institute,
Williamstown, Mass.
Owned by Benjamin Franklin, descended in the family of Henry Hill, Franklin's executor

Union of the colonies is absolutely necessary for their preservation.

—Benjamin Franklin, *Reasons and Motives for the Albany Plan of Union, 1754*

Declaring Independence

From his base in England, Franklin was out of touch with the mood of his countrymen and seriously underestimated the intensity of colonial anger against the Stamp Act of 1765. In a rare misstep, he continued negotiating towards a compromise—but the tensions between the colonies and Great Britain were already irreconcilable.

In 1774, in the wake of the Boston Tea Party and in the midst of colonial cries for "no taxation without representation," Franklin was summoned by solicitor-general Lord Wedderburn to appear before the British Privy Council. There he was accused of treason against the Crown and publicly humiliated—yet Franklin remained silent throughout the ordeal. This was a moment of epiphany, as Franklin came to realize that compromise—for once—was unlikely to carry the day. He left London for the colonies where he added his voice to the growing insurgency. On July 4, 1776, the American colonists declared their independence from Britain.

Thomas Jefferson
Holograph draft of the Declaration of
Independence, July 1776
Manuscript
American Philosophical Society,
Philadelphia

We hold these Truths to be self-evident, that all Men are created equal, that they are endowed by their Creator with certain unalienable Rights, that among these are Life, Liberty, and the Pursuit of Happiness.

—Declaration of Independence, 1776

DECLARATION OF INDEPENDENCE, 1776

The Declaration of Independence was adopted by the Continental Congress on July 4, 1776. It proclaimed to the world that colonial America sought independence from Great Britain. It declared that independence rested on the clearest of principles: that men are created free and equal, and that they cannot legitimately be governed by those to whom they have not given their consent. Thomas Jefferson was the primary author of the document, aided by a committee including Benjamin Franklin, John Adams, Roger Sherman and Robert R. Livingston.

The Declaration of Independence was written, in part, to demonstrate American resolve and solidarity in its formal split from Great Britain. This was important because the colonies needed to persuade potential allies—especially France—to aid the American cause.

When Jefferson drafted the Declaration of Independence, he made exact copies in his own hand as a record. He submitted one of the drafts to Congress on July 1, and seven days later, sent this copy to his friend Richard Henry Lee, a delegate from Virginia, who was, in fact, the first to propose issuing a declaration of independence. Notations in the margins were written by Lee's brother Arthur.

Forming Alliances

The fledgling American army was no match for Britain's well-established military might. In the fall of 1776 Franklin was sent overseas to negotiate a military alliance with the French. In France he capitalized on his scientific fame, networking enthusiastically within the Paris social scene. Franklin became an active member of the Freemasons and developed friendships with General Lafayette and Caron de Beaumarchais. He recognized that to win the cooperation of the French he had to understand their interests and remain humble in demeanor. By wearing a fur cap rather than an elaborate wig, for instance, Franklin cultivated an image of personal modesty and rustic charm.

His strategy paid off. Franklin soon won the support of the foreign minister Comte de Vergennes and King Louis XVI, and in 1778 the Treaty of Amity between America and France was signed. In it France agreed to supply troops, funds, and armaments vital for an American victory against Great Britain.

Jean Baptiste Nini after Thomas Walpole
Portrait medallion of Benjamin Franklin, 1777
Pot metal
Benjamin Franklin Kahn,
Benjamin Franklin Cabinet, Chevy Chase, Md.

The first of many profile portrait medallions to be made of Franklin while he lived in France, this well-known medallion was modeled by Jean Baptiste Nini after Walpole's drawing of Franklin in his fur cap. Numerous copies were made, including a version with spectacles, and two years later, Nini produced another medallion—after a different drawing—without the fur cap.

There shall be a firm, inviolable and universal Peace, and a true and sincere Friendship between the most Christian King, his Heirs and Successors, and the United States of America.

—Treaty of Amity, 1778

TREATY OF AMITY, 1778

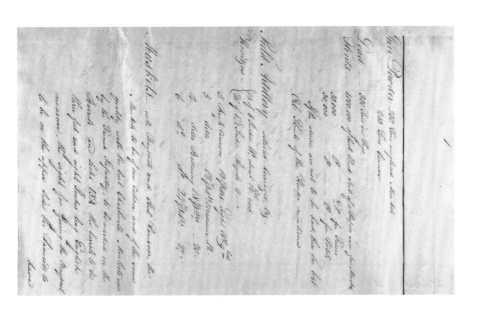

In 1778 the Treaties of Amity and Commerce (commonly known as the Treaty of Amity) produced a strategic alliance between the United States and France, in which each nation agreed to aid one another in the event of British attack. Already at war with Britain, the new American nation needed significant support in the form of loans, military supplies, and troops. The Treaty officially brought France into the American Revolutionary War, providing aid at a crucial time and ultimately enabling the Americans to win their fight for independence. Negotiating the Treaty on behalf of the United States were Benjamin Franklin, Silas Deane, Arthur Lee, and Conrad Alexander Gerard.

Estimate of Stores for the Armye—Estimate N3,
July 1779
Manuscript
The Historical Society of Pennsylvania, Philadelphia

Congress sent Franklin this detailed, 38-page list of supplies to acquire in France. It specified items essential to outfitting and sustaining the American troops, ranging from arms of all sorts to bolts of cloth for uniforms, cooking pots, fifes and drums, and goods for Indian allies—all of which then had to be smuggled across the Atlantic, often via the Caribbean. The first ship, the "Marquis de Lafayette," was captured at sea by a British gun boat, the bounty sold at auction in London, and Franklin had to start all over again. Ultimately, however, Franklin succeeded, and the supplies made their way to America.

Life is a kind of Chess, in which we often have Points to gain, & Competitors or Adversaries to contend with. . . The game is so full of events . . . that one is encouraged to continue the contest to the last, in hopes of Victory from our own skill.

—Benjamin Franklin, *The Morals of Chess*, 1779

Chess set (French), 1750–1780
Pearwood
American Philosophical Society,
Philadelphia
Photo by Peter Harholdt

Owned by Benjamin Franklin;
descended in the family of Deborah
Bache Duane

Mastering Diplomacy

At his residence in the Paris suburb of Passy, Franklin frequently entertained friends, spies, and fellow statesmen while pursuing his passion for chess. Franklin's continued popularity with the French helped guarantee his next diplomatic victory, the 1783 Treaty of Paris, officially ending America's Revolutionary War with Great Britain.

To this diplomatic challenge, Franklin brought a supple and flexible mind and a refined appreciation of the needs of others. Franklin used his understanding of French and British interests to negotiate a treaty to secure peace that was acceptable to all sides. As the negotiations neared conclusion, Franklin wrote to his British friend Sir Joseph Banks, "There never was a good War, or a bad Peace."

TREATY OF PARIS, 1783

Although the Revolutionary War ended with the American victory at Yorktown in the fall of 1781, the terms of peace between Britain and the United States were not formalized until September 3, 1783, when the Treaty of Paris was signed. In the two years between the end of hostilities and the signing of the Treaty, the American negotiators—Benjamin Franklin, John Adams, and John Jay—worked with their British, French, and Spanish counterparts to shape a treaty that guaranteed American sovereignty. The Treaty gave formal recognition to the United States, established its national boundaries, and provided for the evacuation of British troops.

His Brittanic Majesty acknowledges the said United States . . . to be free sovereign and independent.

—Treaty of Paris, 1783

Benjamin West
American Commissioners of the Preliminary Peace Negotiations with Great Britain, 1783–1784
Oil on canvas
Winterthur Museum, Garden and Library, Winterthur, Del.

In the spring of 1783 Benjamin West began a painting to celebrate the signing of the preliminary articles for peace between Great Britain and the United States. The group portrait was originally intended to include the British commissioner Richard Oswald and his secretary Caleb Whitfoord, in addition to the Americans (from left to right): John Jay, John Adams, Benjamin Franklin, Henry Laurens, and Franklin's grandson William Temple Franklin. But Oswald refused to pose, and the painting was never finished.

The navigation of the river Mississippi, from its source to the ocean, shall forever remain free and open to the subjects of Great Britain and the citizens of the United States.

—Article 8, Treaty of Paris, 1783

John Wallis
The United States of America laid down from the best Authorities, Agreeable to the Peace of 1783
London, 1783
Hand-colored engraving and ink
The Historical Society of Pennsylvania, Philadelphia

This is the first map to show the boundaries of the United States as determined by the Treaty of Paris in 1783. It is also the first map to portray the American flag with 13 stars and stripes—evidence of American sovereignty. Franklin is seated in the lower right.

I confess, that I do not entirely approve of this Constitution at present; but Sir, I am not sure I shall never approve it . . . Thus I consent, Sir, to this Constitution, because I expect no better, and because I am not sure that it is not the best.

—*Benjamin Franklin, Speech in the Convention at the Conclusion of its Deliberations, 1787*

Creating a Constitution

Franklin returned to America in 1785 and within two years was once again at the center of the effort to define and shape the new nation. In 1787 he was the oldest member of the Constitutional Convention, suffering from poor health and often excruciating pain. Nonetheless, Franklin's experience as a seasoned diplomat and negotiator, combined with his keen observation of human nature, made him an ideal delegate to the Convention. His most important contributions were his spirit of pragmatic compromise and strong desire for unity. He drew on both to play a significant role in brokering the "Great Compromise"—a legislature of two houses, one elected in proportion to population and one in which each state would have equal representation.

Franklin opposed using landownership as a prerequisite for the right to vote; refused to grant unlimited veto power to the president; and recommended impeachment as a remedy for improper conduct. He believed that the major achievement of the Constitutional Convention was the unification of the states. Although the new Constitution did not have the anti-slavery clause he had hoped for, he signed it nonetheless, "recognizing the greater goal of unity."

WE, the People of the United States, in order to form a more perfect union, establish justice, insure domestic tranquility, provide for the common defence, promote the general welfare, and secure the blessings of liberty to ourselves and our posterity, do ordain and establish this Constitution for the United States of America.

—Constitution of the United States of America, 1787

CONSTITUTION OF THE UNITED STATES, 1787

The first three words of the Constitution—We the People—embody its most striking feature: ultimate political authority resides not in the government or in any single government official, but rather in the people.

The new system of government established by the Framers of the Constitution was based on republican principles. Power was to be distributed among three separate but interdependent branches: the legislative, the executive, and the judicial. Under an elaborate system of checks and balances, each branch has the power to control and check the powers of the other two branches. The Framers further divided power between the federal government and the states.

In 1791 Americans added a list of individual rights to the Constitution. These first ten amendments became known as the Bill of Rights.

"Fugio" penny, 1787
Brass and copper
Collection of the Grand Lodge of Free
and Accepted Masons of Pennsylvania,
Philadelphia
Photo by Peter Harholdt

The first coins issued by the authority of the United States were based on an earlier design suggested by Franklin, which showed the chain of union between the 13 states and was used on currency issued in 1776. The obverse shows a sundial with the legend "Fugio [I fly] 1787 Mind your business" and the reverse reads, "We are one United States."

46

Constitution of the United States
Philadelphia: Dunlap and Claypoole, 1787
Printed broadside with
Benjamin Franklin's handwritten annotations
American Philosophical Society, Philadelphia
Owned by Benjamin Franklin

Fear not Death;
for the sooner we die,
the longer shall we be immortal.

—*Poor Richard's Almanack, 1740*

1787–Today
Seeing Franklin

At 81, Benjamin Franklin was twice the average age of the other members of the Constitutional Convention. Suffering from gout and kidney stones, he nevertheless continued his public career, accepting reelection for his third term as president of the Pennsylvania Assembly and meeting regularly with friends and admirers such as Thomas Jefferson.

In these final years of his life, Franklin remained open-minded and reflective. He renewed work on his autobiography—started years earlier—and served as President of the Pennsylvania Abolition Society, taking a prominent stand against slavery.

Charles Willson Peale
Portrait of Benjamin Franklin, 1787
Oil on canvas
Pennsylvania Academy of the Fine Arts, Philadelphia, Bequest of Mrs. Sarah Harrison (The Joseph Harrison, Jr. Collection)

This is the last known life portrait of Franklin, painted when he was 81 years old, serving as President of the Supreme Executive Council of Pennsylvania and attending sessions of the Constitutional Convention.

I have ever had a Pleasure in obtaining any little Anecdotes of my Ancestors . . . Now imagining it may be equally agreable to you to know the Circumstances of my Life . . . I sit down to write them for you.

—Benjamin Franklin, *Autobiography*

The Most Famous Autobiography of All Time

Though he never finished writing it, Franklin's *Autobiography* is the most widely published memoir in history and has never gone out of print. In his autobiography, which he started as a letter to his son, Franklin offers the story of his life as an archetypal journey from rags to riches. The *Autobiography* remains inspiring today: it documents Franklin's many achievements, details his struggles with personal improvement, explains his belief in personal virtue, and exemplifies his ceaseless self-questioning.

Mémoires de la vie privée de Benjamin Franklin (First French edition)
Paris, 1791
Collection of Stuart E. Karu
Photo by Peter Harholdt

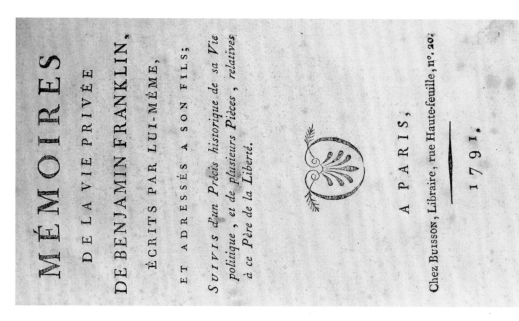

A year after his death, Franklin's manuscript autobiography, which covered the first 25 years of his life, was translated into French and published. It was followed by versions in Swedish (1792), English (1793), an American edition (1794), and eventually dozens of others. Franklin's *Autobiography* is often considered one of the most influential of its genre ever written.

Benjamin Franklin's Epitaph, n.d.
Autograph manuscript
The Papers of Benjamin Franklin

Three versions of Franklin's Epitaph exist in his own hand. This one is believed to be the earliest. Franklin is thought to have first composed his Epitaph in 1728.

When he died 62 years later, Franklin was buried in the cemetery of Christ Church, in Philadelphia. His tombstone is a simple flat slab, bearing only his and Deborah's names.

A Note About Dates

In 1752 Britain and her colonies changed from the Julian to the Gregorian calendar to better synchronize with the true rotation of the earth. In this 11-day adjustment, the day after September 2, 1752, became September 14, and the year now began on January 1, instead of March 25. Thus Franklin's birth date under the old calendar, January 6, 1705, became January 17, 1706. Curiously, when writing copies of his Epitaph, Franklin recognized only the change of year.

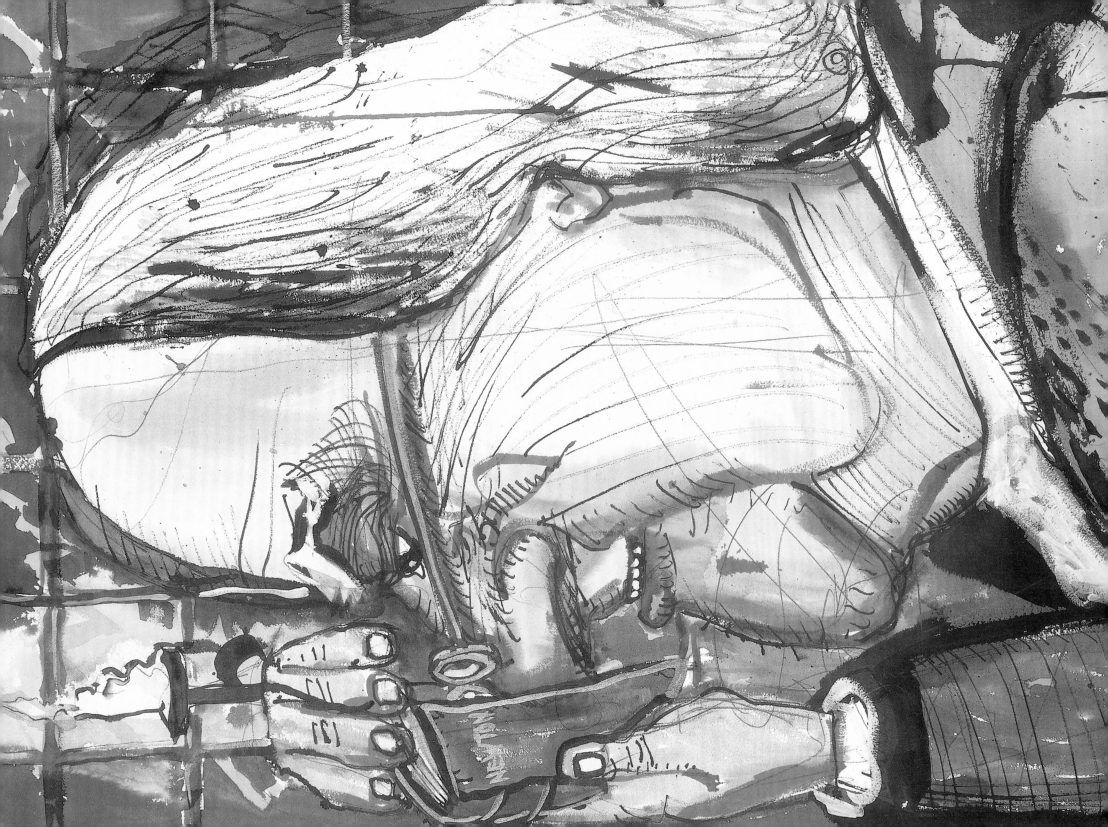

I have sometimes almost wished it had been my destiny to be born two or three centuries hence. For invention and improvement are prolific, and beget more of their kind. Many of great importance, now unthought of, will before that period be produced; and then I might not only enjoy their advantages, but have my curiosity gratified in knowing what they are to be.

—Benjamin Franklin to Rev. John Lathrop, 1788

How the World Sees Franklin

Three centuries after his birth, Franklin's legacy lives on. For much of his own life, Franklin was a pop icon in the colonies and abroad; he was admired and internationally celebrated—even fashionable. After his death, Franklin's image was used to teach lessons, sell products, and promote the principles he embodied: hard work, self-improvement, partnership, and compromise.

Franklin has been memorialized, revered, romanticized, spoofed, and made into an advertising and financial symbol. His face and figure have been depicted in every medium—stone, paint, film, cartoon, the Internet—and can be seen on billboards and building facades, postage stamps, and the $100 bill. More than 30 American states have streets, counties, and towns named after him, and his life is taught in schools around the world. Franklin's name evokes imagination, wit, and entrepreneurial ingenuity worldwide.

As the continuing presence of Franklin's image demonstrates, we will celebrate his ideals and hold his contributions dear for generations to come.

How do you see Franklin?

Benjamin Franklin: A Guide to the Exhibition

The Benjamin Franklin Tercentenary, a non-profit organization supported by a lead grant of $4 million from The Pew Charitable Trusts, was established to mark the 300-year anniversary of Benjamin Franklin's birth (1706–2006) with a celebration dedicated to educating the public about Franklin's enduring legacy and inspiring renewed appreciation of the values he embodied. The Benjamin Franklin Tercentenary was founded in 2000 by a consortium of five Philadelphia cultural institutions: the American Philosophical Society, The Franklin Institute, The Library Company of Philadelphia, the Philadelphia Museum of Art and the University of Pennsylvania. In addition, an Act of Congress in 2002 created the Benjamin Franklin Tercentenary Commission, a panel of fifteen outstanding Americans chosen to study and recommend programs to celebrate Franklin's 300th birthday. The Benjamin Franklin Tercentenary can be found online at www.benfranklin300.org.

Benjamin Franklin Tercentenary Executive Staff

Dr. Rosalind Remer
Executive Director

Dr. Page Talbott
Associate Director

Dana Devon
Director, Educational Programming

Dr. Susan Taylor-LeDuc
European Representative

Nicola Twilley
Director, Public Programming

COVER:
Portrait bust of Benjamin Franklin, marble by Jean Antoine Houdon, 1779. Philadelphia Museum of Art, purchased with a generous grant from The Barra Foundation, Inc., matched by contributions from the Henry P. McIlhenny Fund in memory of Frances P. McIlhenny, the Water E. Stait Fund, the Fiske Kimball Fund, and with funds contributed by Mr. and Mrs. Jack M. Friedland, Hannah L. and J. Welles Henderson, Mr. and Mrs. E. Newbold Smith, Mr. and Mrs. Mark E. Rubenstein, Mr. and Mrs. John J. F. Sherrerd, The Women's Committee of the Philadelphia Museum of Art, Marguerite and Gerry Lenfest, Leslie A. Miller and Richard B. Worley, Mr. and Mrs. John A. Nyheim, Mr. and Mrs. Robert A. Fox, Stephanie S. Eglin, Maude de Schauensee, Mr. and Mrs. William T. Vogt, and with funds contributed by individual donors to the Fund for Franklin, 1996. Photo by Graydon Wood.

BACK COVER:
Benjamin Franklin Drawing Electricity from the Sky, oil on slate by Benjamin West, ca. 1816. Philadelphia Museum of Art, gift of Mr. and Mrs. Wharton Sinkler, 1958. Photo by Graydon Wood.

ENDPAPERS:
The Apotheosis of Benjamin Franklin and George Washington (English), copperplate printed on cotton, ca. 1785. Collection of Robert Staples and Barbara Fahs Charles.